W9-ACQ-220

DISCARDED

784.6
Ar6r

21811

O2

DATE DUE			
Jan 15 '74			
May 16 77K			

Rhythms

FOR THE HOME,
KINDERGARTEN,
AND PRIMARY.

ARRANGED AND COMPILED

BY

FRANCIS M. ARNOLD

DIRECTOR OF MUSIC
CHICAGO KINDERGARTEN COLLEGE.

———

CARL A. RUDISILL
LIBRARY
LENOIR RHYNE COLLEGE

PUBLISHED BY

THE WILLIS MUSIC COMPANY

CINCINNATI, OHIO.

784.6
ArGr

Copying of either the entire, or separate parts of this collection by any process whatsoever is forbidden and is subject to the penalties provided by the copyright law of the United States in force July 1, 1909.

21811
July '46

Dedicated

to my many pupils

in the Kindergarten and

Primary Grades, of the

Chicago Schools

Copyright MCMIX by W. H. Willis & Co.
International Copyright.
Printed in the U. S. A.

Suggestions for Using the Rhythms

This book is the result of many years of experience in teaching Kindergartners and primary teachers to play the piano in their schools. All of the music has been actually used in school by my pupils, and has been found practical. For mothers and others who have not had special training in the use of rhythm, the following suggestions are offered.

QUIET MUSIC. The use of quiet music, and music for prayer on the opening of school, is too well understood to need comment; but the suggestion is offered that mothers in the home play music of this character while their children are going to sleep in the evening. The effect on the child's nervous system, his aesthetic nature, and his disposition, will, I believe, be most beneficial.

MORNING BOWS or SILENT GAME. The children stand in a circle. One child walks quietly to another child and bows; they exchange places, the first child stepping into the circle, the second proceeding to a third child, bowing and taking his place in the circle; the third child bows to a fourth, and so on until all the children have participated. The bowing to music can also be used when it is desired to have the children pass from the circle to the tables. One child is appointed leader, the others pass to the tables one by one, as he bows to them.

MARCHES. In playing for children to march, it is necessary to have clear, strong accents, and what may be called a rhythmic swing; a swing so contagious that it carries the children along in correct time and step. Attention can be trained by varying the touch, at times using a light touch, at times a heavier touch. If the children are inclined to march with a heavy step, this can be corrected through playing with a light touch, and asking them to listen to the piano as they march. The same march should not be used constantly, as the children lose the rhythm when the march becomes monotonous or mechanical, and they grow careless in step and in position of body. The erect position of body is secured in response to the life and spirit put into the music by the pianist. Rag-time and complicated rhythms should be shunned in playing for children.

TIPTOE MARCHES should be played with a light touch. The children march lightly, on tiptoe, making as little sound as possible. On account of the muscular strain this march should be short and not be used too often.

SKIPS. This activity should be light and free. The movement is a "hippity-hop", with the feet alternately leaving the floor. Children at first are inclined to lead with the same foot; in such instances a very simple skip should be used, until they have learned to alternate the feet. The music should be played with a light touch and not too rapidly.

RUNS consist of short, rapid steps in time to music. This rhythm can be used in the various games of driving ponies, or running horses.

GALLOPS and GALLOPING HORSES. One foot leads, and the body is carried forward by a jumping movement. The feet leave the floor together, but the rear foot touches the floor a fraction of a beat before the forward foot. This movement is in imitation of a galloping horse. It is known to most children.

TOURNAMENT GAME. One child stands holding up a hoop. The rest carry spears and gallop as if they were horsemen. As a horseman gallops past, he tries to catch the hoop on his spear without stopping or lessening his speed. By having a supply of hoops at hand, the game can proceed without interruption.

HIGH-STEPPING HORSES. In each step the leg is lifted with the knee bent, the up-movement bringing the knee to a level with the hip. The music must not be too rapid.

HOPS. One foot is held up behind by bending the knee, while the child hops on the other foot in time to music. To avoid fatigue change to the other foot soon. This activity should not be continued long.

FLYING BIRDS. A moderate, running forward movement of the body, with outstretched arms moving slightly up and down, imitating the flying motion of birds. The bird's flight is more direct, and the motion of the wings is shorter and less sweeping than that of the butterfly.

BUTTERFLIES. A running movement which is more rapid than that of the flying birds. The arms move rhythmically up and down, in long sweeps, between a point where the hands come together above the head, and the natural position at the sides of the body. Either the finger tips or the backs of the hands, may meet above the head.

SKATING. Alternate sliding of the feet, without either foot leaving the floor.

GIANTS. A long, heavy stride, which is slow and ponderous. The body is held erect.

SQUIRRELS. A rapid, running movement, imitating a frisking squirrel; stopping now and then, to pick up a nut.

HOBBY-HORSE. One foot in advance, but both feet flat on floor; trunk and head erect. The body moves forward and back, bringing into play the knee and ankle joints.

HEEL AND TOE. Left foot touches heel to floor in front, then toe to floor behind, three short polka steps forward; right foot, heel in front, toe behind, polka step forward, left foot repeats, and so on.

SWINGING. № I. Arms above head as if holding the ropes of a swing; stand with one foot forward; transfer the weight from one foot to the other with a backward and forward rhythmical movement. The knees are not bent. № II. The children are in groups of threes. Two children are placed in front, facing forward, and a very short distance apart. They reach out and clasp the hands which are toward each other. The third child, who is placed back of them, reaches forward and grasps the clasped hands of the front children with one of his hands. The three children swing back and forth, keeping the rhythm of the music.

ROLLING BALLS TO MUSIC. The children are seated in a circle, and roll balls back and forth to each other, starting the ball on the first beat of the measure. This develops a sense of rhythm.

BOUNCING BALLS. The children stand or march, bouncing balls on the first beat of the measure.

HUNTING THE BALL. The children are seated in a circle. One child leaves the room. The ball is hidden between the hands of a child in the circle. The music begins softly when the first child returns; as he nears the place where the ball is hidden the music grows louder, until he finds it. Should he pass it by, the music grows fainter until he nears it again.

I wish to acknowledge indebtedness for valuable suggestions, to Miss Frances Wetmore Director of Games, Chicago Kindergarten College.

Francis Marion Arnold

Contents

Skips

Runs

Galops

Tournaments

Hops

Prayer

WEBER

Andante in E

BEETHOVEN

Austrian Hymn

HAYDN

Poco Adagio cantabile

Twenty-third Psalm

MENDELSSOHN

Child's Prayer

FR. BEHR

Morning Prayer

STREABBOG

PART I
Andante

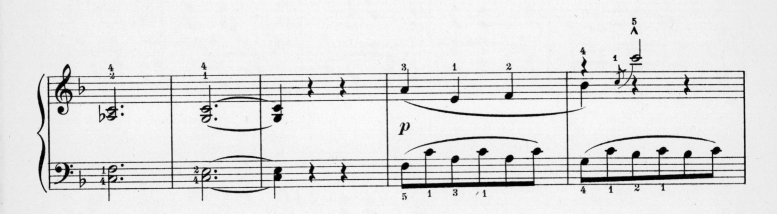

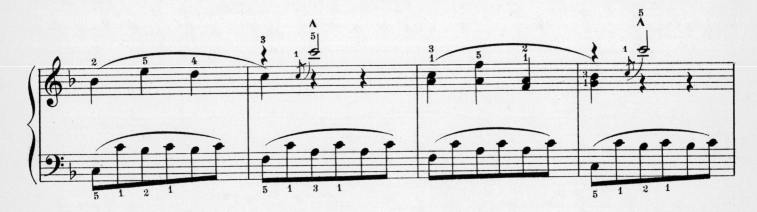

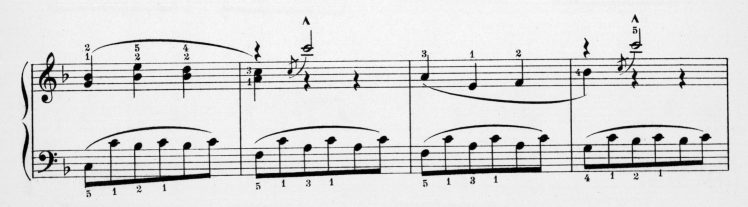

This selection is too long to be **used** entire. It can be divided into two or even three parts.

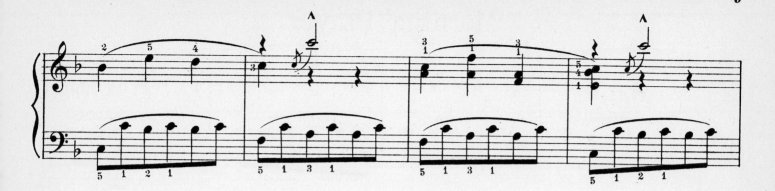

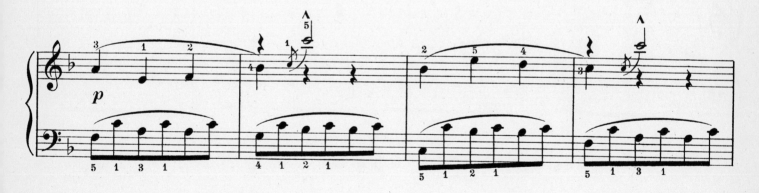

PART II

ben marcato il canto

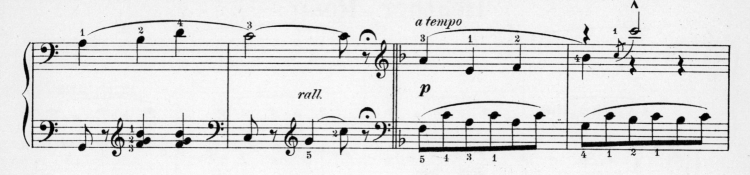

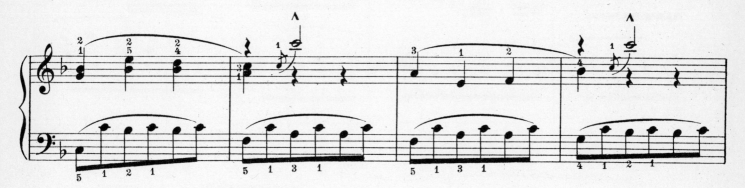

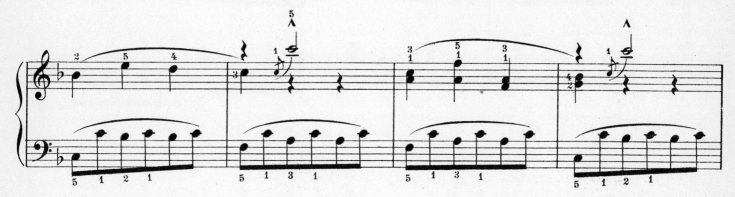

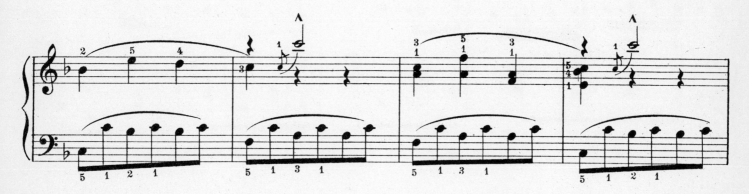

Più lento

Heather Rose

SCHUBERT

Andantino

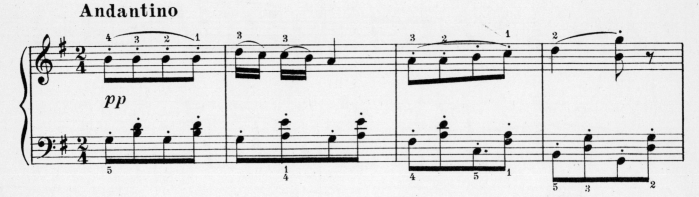

Meditation

HAYDN

Allegretto quasi Andante

Andante in F

BEETHOVEN

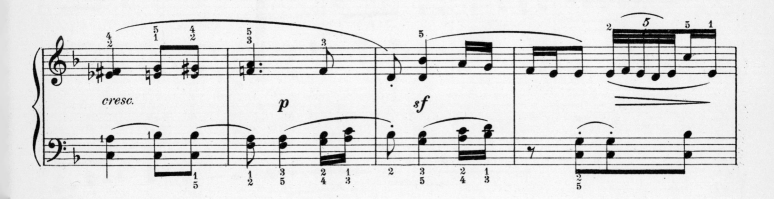

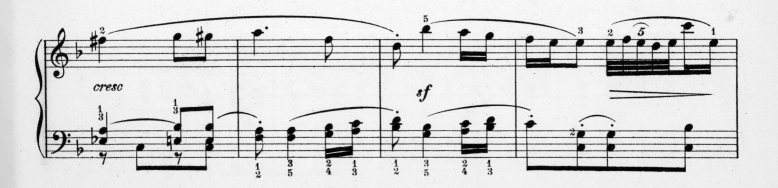

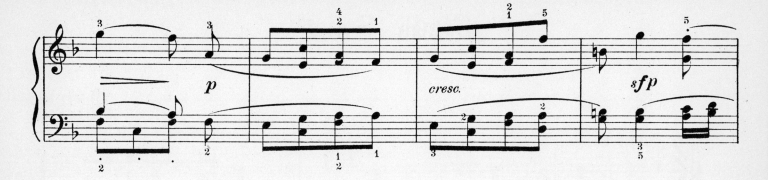

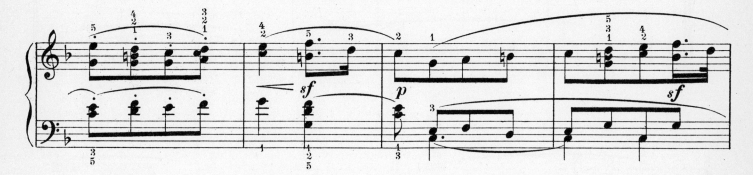

Cradle Song

OESTEN

Morning Bows

Arranged from "Floating Zephyrs"

ENGELMANN

Tempo I

Fine

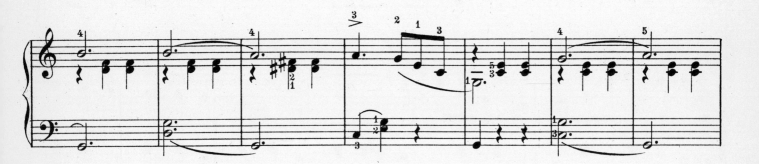

D. C. al Fine

Hand in Hand

March

RUMMEL

Tempo di Marcia

Soldier's March

FRANZ ADLER

Moderato

D.C. al fine

First Grade March

FRANZ ADLER

March

Cadets March

LANGE

Allegro moderato *with humor*

Drum

With Bugle and Drum

March

LOESCHHORN

Tempo di Marcia

1182

Standard Bearer

March

SMITH

In quick time

Fine

D.C. al fine

Young Sentinel
March

ENGELMANN

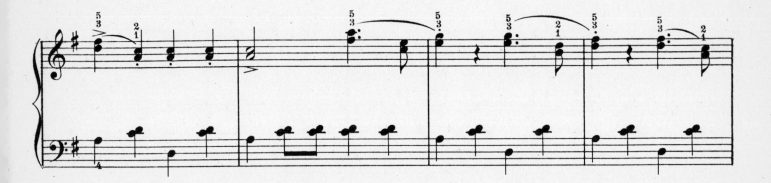

Maestoso

D.C. al fine

Festival March

SMITH

In quick time

Fine

D. C.

Little Ensign

March

GIESE

Tempo di Marcia

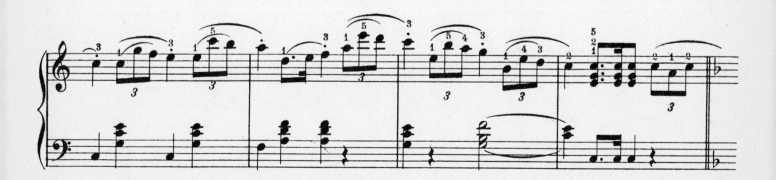

Passing Troops March

OEHMLER

Tempo di Marcia

Fine

Follow the Leader

March

SUPPE

Fine

Fine

Review March

RESCH

D.C.

Vienna March

SCHRAMMEL

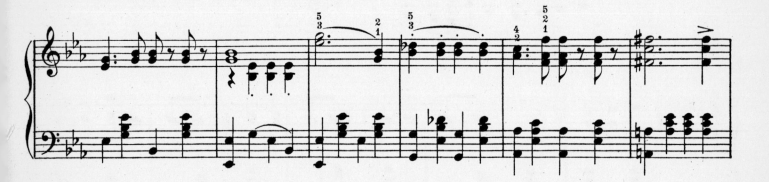

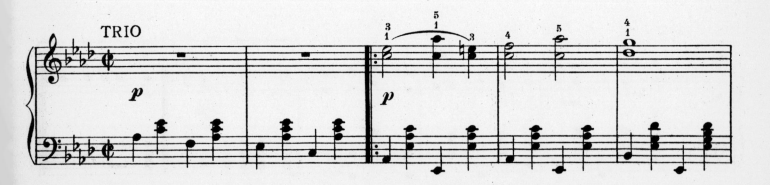

Marcia D.C. al Fine

Tip- toe March

FRANZ ADLER

Light staccato

March and Skip

Arranged from
Gounod's Faust

March

con spirito

SKIP
Allegro

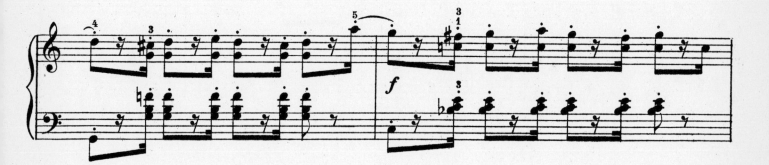

Repeat Skip

D.C. al Fine

Skip
Arranged from
Calla-Lily March

SPAULDING

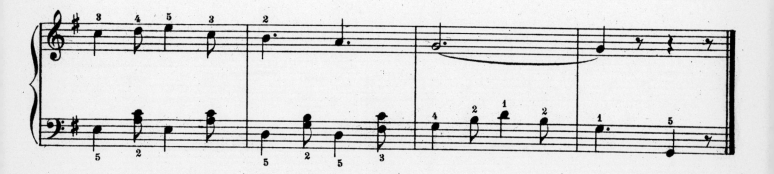

Skip

Arranged from

London Bridge is Falling Down

Rapidly

BREYER

"Lon - don Bridge is   fall - ing   down,

fall - ing down,   fall - ing down,   Lon don Bridge is   fall - ing down   my   fair

la - dy."

Through the Clover

Skip

OESTEN

Rapidly

Marionettes
Skip

OESTEN

Kerry Dance

Skip

MOLLOY

Allegro

Skip
Arranged from
Thistle down Two-Step

READ

Brightly

1182

D.C.

Skip

Arranged from

Flowers of the Forest

BURNS

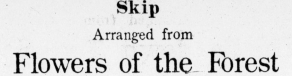

Skip
Arranged from
Rustic Dance

Allegretto

HOWELL

con Pedale

Promenade and Skip

Selection of Partners

FRANZ ADLER

Allegretto

SKIP

Playing Tag

A Run

FRANZ ADLER

Fine

D.C. al Fine

Catch Me

A Run

LICHNER

A Run

Arranged from

Joyous Farmer

SCHUMANN

Happy Children

Galop

STREABBOG

Quick and lightly

Grace notes may be omitted

In Haste

Galop

VOLTI

Wild Ride

Galop

ENGELMANN

Galop

Animato

Fine

March of the Sleepy-Heads

Galop

SPAULDING

78

1182

Galloping Horses

ROGERS

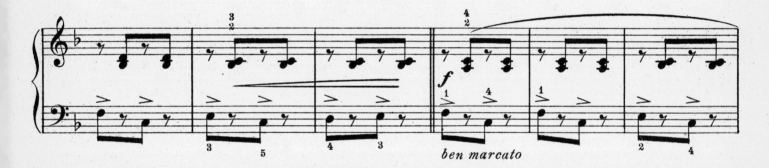

How Peggy came to Town

SMITH

The Jolly Rider
Tournament

LICHNER

Fine

D.C. al fine

Tournament

Arranged from

The Huntsman's Song

SCHUMANN

Allegro animato

A - riding we will go

Tournament

WARREN

High-stepping Horses

Arranged from BEETHOVEN

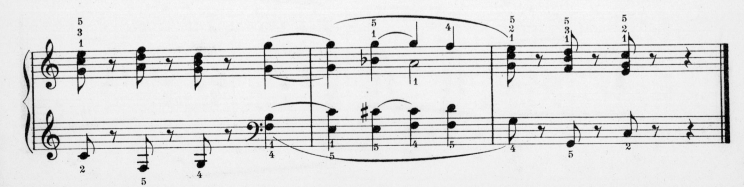

A Hop

Little Hop o' my Thumb

ADLER

Always staccato

A Hop
Hopscotch

STREABBOG

A Hop
Grasshoppers

Arranged from HAYDN

Allegro con spirito

Flying Birds
Little One's Dream

Arranged from CRAMER

Moderato

Flying Birds

CZIBULKA

Flying Birds
Swallows

GILLET

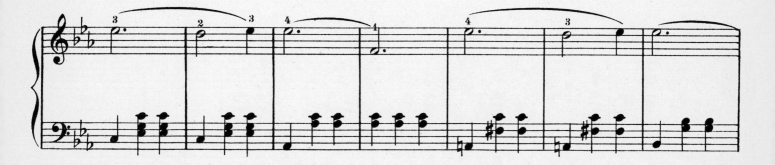

Butterflies
Melody in F

Arranged from RUBINSTEIN

Not too rapidly

Fine

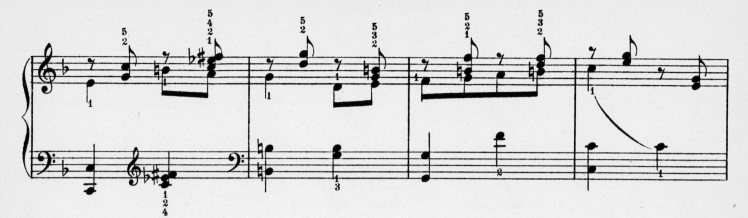

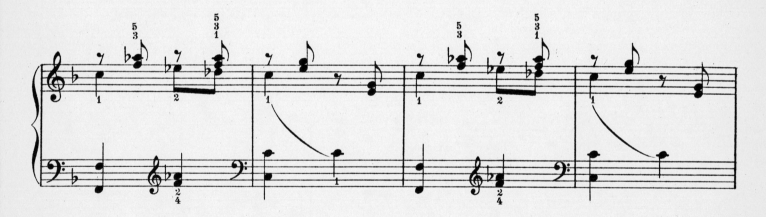

D. C. al fine

Butterflies
Spring Song

Arranged from MENDELSSOHN

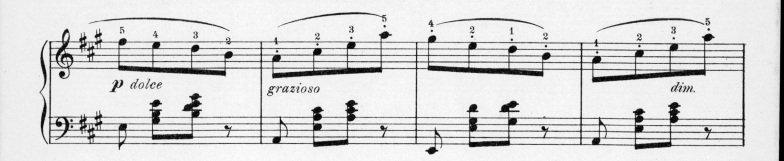

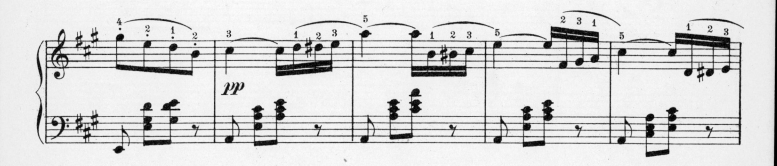

Butterflies

Arranged from HELLER

Not too fast

Skating

ROEDER

CARL A. RUDISILL
LIBRARY
LENOIR RHYNE COLLEGE

Giants

Arranged from HANDEL

Slowly and majestically

Squirrels

Arranged from HELLER

Allegro vivace ♩= 104

The Hobby Horse

ADLER

Moderato

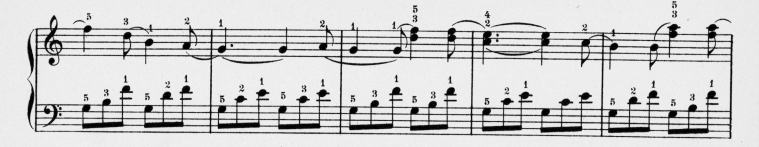

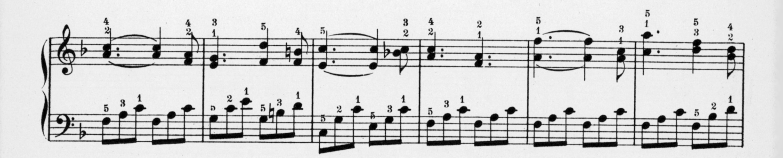

Heel and Toe

LICHNER

Allegretto scherzando

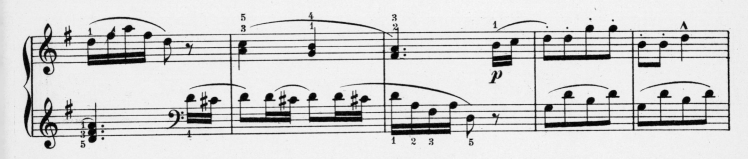

Swinging № I

SCHUBERT

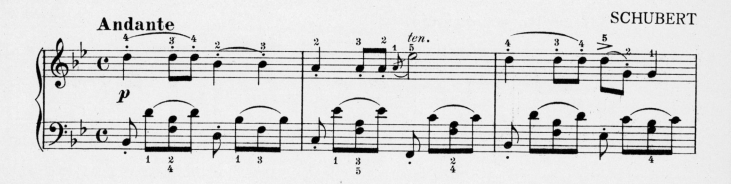

Swinging Nº II

ROEDER

Rolling Balls or Bouncing Balls

ROEDER

Hunting the Ball

Arranged from

Soft Southern Breezes

Valse Reverie

KARL BENDL

Andante moderato

TUNES
FROM
MANY LANDS
A First Solo and Duet Book for PIANO
By ANGELA DILLER and ELIZABETH QUAILE

The object of this book is to provide beginners in piano playing with interesting material of real musical value.

In the opinion of the authors, Folk-Music is the most appropriate material for the child's first study. This music comes from the childhood of the race. A young student whose taste is trained by hearing and playing beautiful old melodies will easily develop an appreciation of the masterpieces of musical literature of which these are the fore-runners. —*Angela Diller and Elizabeth Quaile*

The difficulty of all piano teachers is finding ideal solo material with which to supplement methods.

"Ideal solo material" for young students consists of short pieces of interesting melody and attractive form, coupled with authoritative and sound musicianship.

National Songs and Folk-Music of the world suitably arranged supply the need perfectly.

"Tunes from Many Lands," as its title implies, consists entirely of such songs and music. It contains 54 solos and 19 duets presented in a fashion that stands for the "last word" in modern educational books for elementary piano study. The editing is admirable; the grading careful; the taste faultless.

Educators can use the volume supplementally to any method, whether established or original, because its soundness permits its ready adaptation to any system.

The pieces help to develop every phase of elementary technic, and familiarize the pupil early with the various elements to be found in the music he will meet later.

"Tunes from Many Lands" also possesses many excellent innovations, both in ideas and in their presentation, impossible to describe here. Because of this fact, the book should be thoroughly examined by educators everywhere.

It grades from the beginning to the end of first grade.

Special Feature

As far as practical the original texts, or English translations of them, have been placed at the top of the Songs and Tunes. These lines indicate the rhythm of the piece itself, and also suggest the spirit in which it should be interpreted.

Price $1.00 in U.S.A.

The Willis Music Company
137 West Fourth Street   Cincinnati, O.

COLLECTIONS EVERY PARENT CHILD and TEACHER SHOULD HAVE

FOR PLAY AND CALISTHENIC USE

ARNOLD'S COLLECTIONS OF RHYTHMS

For the Home, Kindergarten and Primary

COMPILED BY

FRANCIS M. ARNOLD

The urgent need in the school and at home for good music, suitably arranged so that the parent or teacher will have no difficulty in playing for the children, has made this book possible.

Too often, popular or commonplace music is used in accompanying the marches, games or drills of the little ones.

This collection, with the descriptive preface, is arranged to meet such demands in every way, and music of the better class is here furnished for every hour—from morning prayer through all the games of the day.

Price, Cloth Binding, $1.50

CHILD LIFE IN MUSIC

A COLLECTION OF

PLAYS, DANCES AND GAMES
For the Home, Primary and Kindergarten

COMPILED BY

FRANCIS M. ARNOLD

Of all three elements of music, rhythm, melody and harmony, rhythm makes the most direct appeal, as the child is in the rhythmic stage. Rhythm must therefore be simple and continuous, for a child can not follow when rhythm is broken or intricate. CHILD LIFE IN MUSIC is a work to be used in conjunction with the same author's "Collection of Rhythms." The music is a trifle more pretentious than its companion, but marked with the same good taste and simplicity.

Price, Cloth Binding, $1.50

FESTIVALS AND PLAYS OF CHILDREN

A series of Rhythmic Plays and Dances arranged according to the seasons of the year

BY

FRANCIS M. ARNOLD

In selecting, adapting and writing the various rhythms in this book, Mr. Arnold has studied the free rhythmic expression of children and has caught the essential elements of their representations. Mr. Arnold's rhythms have simplicity of form, the repetition so dear to the child in verse, song or story, the purity of tone and true approximation to the emotions of child life characteristic of the folk music. His arrangement by seasons provides for growth in appreciation and for increasingly difficult production as well as suggesting appropriate music for the more pronounced interests of children at the various times of year. This book also contains numerous selections to be played to the children. These include music for Prayer, Quiet Period and also to illustrate stories and talks.

Price, Cloth Binding, $1.50

MOTHER GOOSE SINGING GAMES

For School Story Hour, Pageants, Home or Plays

BY

PAUL BLISS

Nineteen rhymes, dear to the heart of every child, have been set to simple and refreshing new music. A preface supplies additional instructions for costuming for pageants or plays. The music is so replete with the spirit of the genuine nursery song that any child, no matter how young, can easily master it.

Price, 75 cents

SINGING GAMES AND DANCES

For Schools and Playgrounds

COMPILED AND ARRANGED BY

CARL ZIEGLER, M. D., B. S. G.

The educational value of singing games and dances was recognized long ago by kindergartners, but only in recent years, however, have such games and dances been adopted for use in primary grades. From a mass of available material only such were chosen which experience had proven to be valuable and also usable in schools.

Price, 60 cents

PUBLISHED BY
THE WILLIS MUSIC COMPANY

CINCINNATI OHIO